BIRD FAMILIES

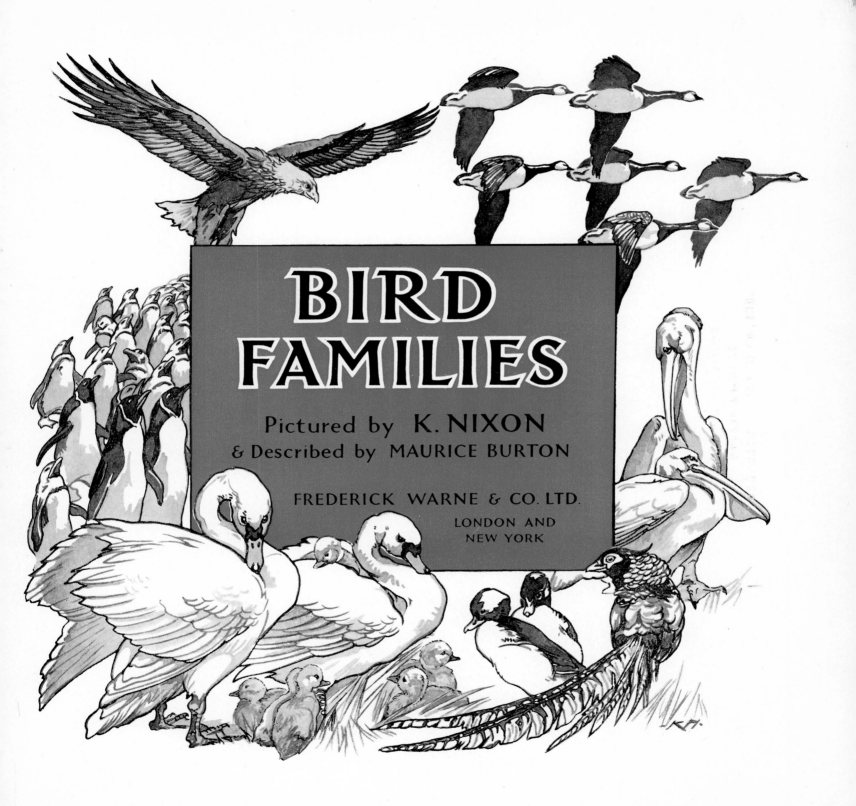

BIRD FAMILIES

Pictured by **K. NIXON**

& Described by MAURICE BURTON

FREDERICK WARNE & CO. LTD.

LONDON AND
NEW YORK

TO TERRY
WITH LOVE

LIBRARY OF CONGRESS CATALOG CARD NUMBER 62-18913

PRINTED IN GREAT BRITAIN

❧ CONTENTS ❧

GOLDFINCH

THERE is not a single black mark against the goldfinch. Most of the year it feeds on the seeds of troublesome weeds such as thistles, and in spring it feeds on insects. When it builds its nest of moss and lichens in the orchard trees it lines it with thistledown.

A goldfinch is also one of our most beautiful birds, with its head marked in crimson, black and white, and with the golden bar on its wing. If you happen to look into a goldfinch nest when the young have hatched, as likely as not the father, fearful of the safety of his youngsters, will try to frighten you away. He does this by drooping his wings, turning his body from side to side and flashing that lovely golden bar at you.

The nestling finch is not a patch on its parents for beauty. Like all nestlings it is ungainly and clumsy and it is covered with a blackish-grey down, but this ball of ugliness will one day shed its downy covering and we shall see that golden bar on the wings. There is, however, just one patch of colour on this ugly nestling. When it opens its beak it shows the crimson lining and dark violet roof of its mouth.

Distribution: British Isles (there is also a Continental species)

LONG-TAILED TIT

THE long-tailed tit is one of the easiest birds to recognize. It goes about its business, not particularly bothered if anyone is near, and it is easy to see in spite of its size. Although it is nearly six inches long, more than half of this is tail, and you can also tell it at once because of its pink and white plumage marked with black.

Although it weighs only a quarter of an ounce, it builds a nest as large as a man's fist—a hollow ball of moss held together by cobwebs and decorated with lichens. The nest is more egg-shaped than round, with a spout-like entrance near the top, and because its shape is said to resemble that of an old-fashioned bottle, the long-tailed tit is sometimes called the bottle-tit.

The nest is lined with small feathers, as many as two thousand or more, and every one is neatly arranged. But it seems that the bottle-tit believes in large numbers. The hen lays anything up to a dozen eggs, and when these hatch into a dozen nestlings you would expect the nest to be rather over-crowded—yet, even so, at night not only does the mother and her large family sleep inside this nest but the father joins them.

Distribution: British Isles (there is also a Continental species)

BLUE TIT

A BLUE TIT is very small, only four and a half inches long, and it can squeeze into the smallest holes. When it starts to build its nest in April it looks around for holes in trees or in a bank. If these fail, it may choose some very odd place for blue tits have been known to nest in an old pump or a hollow iron post. In such places, the nest, made of moss and grass and lined with hair, wool and feathers, may hold up to fourteen eggs, white with reddish-brown speckles. For a fortnight the hen covers this large batch of small eggs to keep them warm, her mate bringing food to her. At the end of that time the eggs hatch and both parents spend the daylight hours finding thousands of insects to feed their large family.

We see the two parents flying to and from the nest for days and we know that when they go in through the very small hole in the top of the iron post or the pump, they are going down to feed nestlings that are two or more feet below. What we have yet to learn is how these youngsters, ready for their first flight, scramble up and squeeze through that tiny opening at the top.

Distribution: British Isles (there is also a Continental species)

MEADOW PIPIT AND CUCKOO

EVERYONE knows how the hen cuckoo lays her eggs in the nest of some small song-bird, and how the young cuckoo throws out the rightful eggs by getting its shoulders under each in turn and hoisting them over the edge. Meadow pipits are often plagued in this way, and we see them working hard, collecting food to satisfy this enormous nestling that does not really belong to them. As the pipit is only 5¾ inches long the baby cuckoo is bigger than its two foster-parents put together.

The surprising thing is that small birds should allow themselves to be put on in this way, but that is not the only surprise. The young cuckoo keeps up an incessant clamour for food, making a noise like a squeaky bicycle pump. Other small birds, not its foster-parents, hearing this sound, often stop and give the cuckoo the food they were carrying to their own nestlings in a nearby nest.

Distribution of cuckoo: Africa (in winter) to Europe (in Summer)

Distribution of meadow pipit: Europe and Asia

MISTLE-THRUSH

THE mistle-thrush is larger than the song-thrush which everybody knows so well. The dark spots on its breast are also bolder. But when you are in doubt that the thrush you are looking at is a mistle-thrush or a song-thrush look for the white tips on the outer feathers of the tail. Only a mistle-thrush has these.

In March each year the mistle-thrushes start their soft and gentle song. This is not as musical as that of the song-thrush, and they repeat it all day and every day until it becomes quite monotonous.

Mistle-thrushes nest early. Some of them start as early as February, building a nest of grass stalks, roots and moss with earth mixed in to strengthen it. This is lined with grass. Usually it is in the fork of a tree or on a bough, but it is sometimes built in a hedge or even in creepers growing on a house.

Four eggs are laid, cream to blue blotched with brown, and although only the hen sits on them the cock keeps close by. They hatch in fourteen days but it is another fortnight before the young birds leave the nest, and during this time both parents feed them.

Distribution: Europe, Asia

PIED FLYCATCHER

THE male pied flycatcher is black with white on his forehead and on his front, and a white bar on his wing. His mate is much less showy, being a dingy brown except for her white front and the bar on the wing. But then she does most of the work. She builds the nest herself and sits on the five to seven pale blue eggs, alone for nearly two weeks.

However, the male is not so negligent as this would make him appear. Pied flycatchers come north from Africa in April or May, and the male is the first to arrive. He it is who searches for and chooses the place where the nest shall be built, and he will boldly drive off even larger birds that might usurp it. And although he leaves the hen to incubate the eggs he feeds her while she is sitting and helps to feed the nestlings as soon as they are hatched.

Distribution: Europe, Asia, Africa

MAGPIE

MAGPIES rob other birds' nest but they seem to take good care that other birds shall not easily tamper with theirs. Anyone who has handled a magpie, even a tame one, will know the sharpness of its bill and how quick it is to nip and nip again, drawing blood each time. So a pair of magpies should be able to drive almost anything away from their nest.

Yet magpies are not satisfied until they have built their nest either high up in a tall tree or, for preference, in a thorn bush. The nest of sticks is bulky, lined with mud and on top of this a layer of fine roots. As if to make it even more secure for their youngsters they usually put a dome over it, and as often as not this is made of thorny twigs.

Within this natural fortress, in April or sometimes even in March, the hen lays five to six eggs, greenish-blue or greyish-green and spotted with brown and grey. The hen incubates the eggs without help from her mate, although he is usually near at hand and readily flies to the nest if she calls. The nestlings are hatched at the end of eighteen days, and then he helps her to feed them for nearly a month.

Distribution: Europe

GREAT SPOTTED WOODPECKER

THE great spotted woodpecker, or pied woodpecker, is one of the three woodpeckers found in Britain. The other two are the green woodpecker, a foot long, and the lesser spotted woodpecker, five inches long, the pied being nine inches long. They all nest in holes in trees, laying four to seven white eggs on the bare floor of the cavity. The hen pied woodpecker does most of the incubating, although the male takes a share, especially at night. The eggs hatch on the sixteenth day and then both parents combine their efforts to feed the chicks with insects.

Perhaps the first inkling you have that there is a nest in a tree is from a sound, like a pair of rusty scissors being used, that seems to come from nowhere. By carefully listening you at last locate the hole in the tree, several feet above head height. You then hide and watch, and before long one of the parents flies in, landing on the trunk below the hole with an insect grub in its beak. At the same time several smaller clamouring beaks appear at the hole. The parent woodpecker puts the grub in one of these and flies off for more.

Distribution: British Isles (there is also a Continental species)

LAPWING

THE lapwing, also known as the green plover or the peewit, nests on the ground. The nest is simply a hollow in the earth, lined with grass stalks, which may be found in a meadow, on ploughed land, on the moors or in the marshes. In this simple nest the hen lays four eggs, stone-coloured or olive green with black spots. For nearly a month the parents take turns at sitting on the eggs, but after they are hatched the hen looks after the chicks alone. All the father does is to keep guard over them.

Lapwing chicks are able to run soon after they are hatched, and they can also feed themselves. They are covered with a brownish down streaked with black, but they have white on the throat and chest. When danger threatens the hen calls to the chicks who crouch with their heads drawn back to hide their white throats so that they are not easy to see in the shadows in the grass. If caught in the open they run for shelter on hearing the parent's alarm call. Meanwhile both mother and father lapwings fly up and swoop at the enemy, trying to take its attention away from the chicks.

Distribution: Europe, Asia, North Africa (and occasionally North America)

PARTRIDGE

A HOLLOW in the ground scraped by the hen and lined with dry grass and dead leaves is all the partridge has for a nest. It may be at the bottom of a hedge, among grass or growing crops, or sheltered by bushes and coarse plants. In this she lays from nine to twenty eggs, sometimes even as many as twenty-three, and she incubates them herself, with no help from the cock until they begin to hatch. She does not begin to sit until all the eggs are laid and it takes twenty-three to twenty-five days before they hatch. All the chicks hatch within a few hours, and it is then that the male partridge may help, by brooding those babies that have left the shell first. An hour or two after the last is hatched, this numerous brood attended by their parents, leave the nest, to search for seeds and small insects. Partridge chicks are not able to fly until they are sixteen days old, although they can run about within a few hours, and begin to flutter their wings after ten days.

Distribution: Europe

MUTE SWAN

THE large nests, which swans make from heaps of reeds and water plants beside rivers and ponds, usually hold five to seven eggs by the time that April or May comes round. The pen, the female, sits closely on them, her mate, the cob, keeping close to guard her, driving off anything that comes near. He does not feed her but he takes his place on the eggs at regular intervals, usually at night, so that she may go off and find food.

The large eggs, four to five inches long and tinged greyish or greenish-blue, take five weeks to hatch. The cygnets, the young swans, covered with greyish-brown down, stay in the nest for a day or two before taking to the water. Since the eggs are laid on alternate days the cygnets do not hatch all at once, and the first out are taken to swim by the cob while the pen continues to sit.

The cygnets stay a long time with the parents. At first they look like downy ducks, but as the weeks pass their necks grow longer, when there is no mistaking them. All this time the pen and the cob look after their brood, the pen tearing up roots and grasses for them to pick up and eat. Then, at the end of nearly five months, the cygnets find that they must look after themselves for the cob, who has been a devoted father, suddenly turns against them and drives them away.

Distribution: Europe

SHELDUCK

THE shelduck is nearly two feet long and has a boldly marked pattern of black, white and chestnut on its body and a red bill and pink feet. It can sometimes be seen on waters inland but it breeds near the sea where there are mud flats and sand dunes. Its nest may be in a rabbit burrow or among bramble and furze, sometimes under rocks or hedges. The nest is made of pale grey down and in this are laid the eight to sixteen creamy-white eggs, which the duck incubates on her own for a month. Twice a day the drake calls to the duck she then leaves the nest to feed while he stays near to guard the eggs.

When the ducklings hatch they are led to the water, as is usual. Sometimes the duck leads them, sometimes both parents, and then we see a procession with the duck leading the way, and the drake following, with the ducklings coming along behind. At times several broods of ducklings may be seen all banded together with only one duck and a drake looking after them.

Distribution: Europe and Asia

CANADA GOOSE

ALTHOUGH its native home is in North America, the Canada goose was brought to Britain in the eighteenth century. It is a large grey-brown goose with a black neck and a black head with a white patch on each side. Its nest is near the water, usually in the shelter of bushes, and is lined with grass, reeds, down and feathers. The eggs usually number five to six, but may be as many as eleven. They are white or creamy-white, and they take a month to hatch. The gander takes no part in the incubating but he stays near the nest on guard.

As is usual with geese, and also with swans and ducks, the chicks, or goslings as the babies are called, do not stay long in the nest. When they first come out of the egg their down is wet, and as soon as this has dried they make their way down to the water, led by the goose. She looks after them for six weeks, leading them about, helping them to find food and sheltering them under her wings when they need to rest. But the gander is never far away. He is always on guard, ready to spring to their defence—and if you have ever tried to go near a gander you will know how hard he can jab with his beak.

Distribution: Alaska, Canada, northern U.S.A.

GREAT CRESTED GREBE

YOU have to be very lucky to get close to the nest of a great crested grebe.

It is a floating mass of decaying weed moored among reeds on a lake, usually well away from the shore.   Both parents take turns at sitting on the eggs, but if you go anywhere near the nest the sitting bird quickly covers the eggs with weed, slides over the side and dives out of sight.

The four young grebes when hatched are covered with cinnamon-coloured down, striped with black.   Both parents feed them and when they are six weeks old they are able to dive themselves and do so at the slightest sign of danger, making sure that they come to the surface again at a spot among the reeds.

The best chance of seeing baby grebes is, therefore, when the parents are giving them a pick-a-back ride.   They sit on the mother's or father's back, between their wings, and so travel about without getting their feet wet.

Distribution: Europe, Asia, Africa, Australia

WHITE PELICANS

PELICANS nest in colonies which may be as much as twenty miles long and five miles across, containing millions of birds. The nest is made of sticks, and two to four pale blue eggs are laid in it. Six weeks later these hatch into naked babies looking more like prehistoric reptiles than birds.

It was believed, centuries ago, that pelicans fed their young by pecking their breasts until the blood ran, so that the chicks could feed on the blood. Of course, there is no truth in this. Pelicans feed on fish which they catch by using the large pouch under the beak as a drag-net. They feed their young with the fish, but it is partly digested. The parent pelican swallows the fish and then brings it up again, and the nestling pushes its beak into the parent's throat to take this half-digested food.

While the nestlings are very young they need very special feeding which is supplied by both the mother and the father. They come to the nest, gently nudge a nestling with the tip of their huge bill, and when the young one raises its head, the parent dribbles a watery fluid into its beak. It is only later that the youngsters take the food for themselves from the parent's throat.

Distribution: Tropical America, India and Australia

CASSOWARY

WE usually expect a hen bird to take the greatest share in bringing up the young, but matters are different with the cassowary. This is a relative of the ostrich and like it is unable to fly, but it can run swiftly on its long, strong legs. Its body is covered with dark coarse feathers, its neck and head are bare, and on the top of its head is a helmet, a bony crest covered with naked skin. The female cassowary is about five feet high, the male slightly smaller, but it is he that does all the work. He scrapes a shallow saucer in the ground and in this the female lays three to four dark green eggs—and then departs. The male incubates the eggs, sitting on them for two months, and when the chicks hatch he tends them alone. The chicks are at first striped and patterned with brown markings and are difficult to see when they crouch on the ground, perfectly still. They like water and swim from an early age.

Distribution: Australia, New Guinea

HERON

ALTHOUGH herons are usually seen in ones and twos, wading in water to catch fish or frogs, they come together at nesting-time. Many pairs build their nests in clumps of trees, in what is called a heronry. The nest is made of sticks and the first year it is not very big, but as the same nest is used year after year it eventually becomes very large and bulky.

The hen lays three to five greenish-blue eggs at intervals of two days and these eggs take nearly a month to hatch. The parents share the incubation. When the change over takes place there is quite a ceremony. The parent that has been away feeding flies to the nest and lands beside it. The one that has been sitting on the eggs stands up. They bob and bow to each other for a few minutes, then one steps out of the nest and the other steps in, settling down on the eggs.

The parents continue to share the work after the chicks have hatched. At first they come to the nest with food in their throats. A nestling seizes the parental bill in its own, and this is the signal for the parent to bring the food up into its bill, at the same time opening the bill slightly. Then the chick is able to help itself from the side.

Distribution: Europe, Asia, Africa

BLACK-NECKED STORK

WE think of storks as white because the common stork that nests in Europe is white, but even that has some black at the tips of the wings. The black-necked stork is almost entirely black except for some white mainly on the shoulders and thighs. Like all other storks it frequents marshy ground, feeding on almost anything it can pick up, especially the small animals, such as frogs and lizards. Its nest is a large platform of sticks in a tree and on this three to four white eggs are laid, the parents sharing the incubation which lasts for a month. The young are almost naked when hatched and they remain in the nest until they are well grown, which means until they are two months or more old.

Both parents bring food to the nest in their throats, but the youngsters have to pick it up for themselves, for the parent bird brings the food up from the throat into its bill and then drops it into the nest, or else it shakes its head from side to side, slightly opening the beak and scattering pieces of food about the nest for its brood.

Distribution: India, Ceylon, Malaya

ROSEATE SPOONBILL

FROM the odd shape of its bill you can tell that the spoonbill must have an unusual way of feeding. It wades in shallow water holding its spoon-shaped bill half-open in the water and swinging its head from side to side. In this way it spoons up freshwater shrimps, water insects, small fishes, frogs and any other small animals of this kind.

The roseate spoonbills make their nest of sticks in a tree, usually in the mangroves. Four eggs are laid in it and these are white, blotched with brown. For three weeks the parents take turns in sitting on them and when the chicks hatch, covered with a white down, they are unable to look after themselves.

Now, a bird with a bill shaped like a spoon is not going to find it easy to feed its chicks in the usual way, so the spoonbill fills its crop with food, goes back to the nest and brings the food up from its crop into its beak, where the chick can take it. As the chick grows, however, it pushes its bill down the parent's throat and takes the food straight from the crop.

Distribution: North and South America

PENGUINS

PENGUINS all look very much alike, differing mainly in size and in the markings on the head and neck. They are very different, however, in the way they look after their eggs and young. The three-foot high emperor penguin of the Antarctic continent makes no nest. It holds its one egg on its feet where it is kept warm by a fold of skin from the parent's body. When the chick hatches it also is held in this way until it is old enough to stand on its own feet—on the ice.

The jackass penguin, two and a half feet high, which lives in the warmer climate of the Falkland Islands, digs a burrow three or four yards long in the sandy cliff. The egg is laid in a rough nest of grass and sticks in a chamber at the end of the burrow.

All penguins are devoted parents, sharing the care of both eggs and chicks. They feed the chicks on fish or squid, the chick pushing its beak into the parent's throat to take it.

Distribution: Southern Hemisphere

KINGFISHER

MOST birds have an easy way of giving each of their offspring its fair share of food.   As soon as they land on the nest, or near it, the nestlings open their beaks wide and stretch up their heads, all in one movement.   The more hungry they are the more they push up their heads on their thin, scraggy necks, so the most hungry is almost bound to be first fed.

But the Kingfishers have an even better system.   These birds scratch a tunnel in a sandy bank, either the river bank or one close to a river.   This may be three feet long and at its inner end is the nesting chamber in which the hen lays her six to eight white eggs.   Both parents need to work hard, catching enough fish, and bringing them to the nest, to feed the hungry youngsters.   So they must lose no time in handing it over and in the darkness of the tunnel it might be difficult for the kingfisher to tell which nestling to feed without a lot of hesitation and fumbling.

The nestlings themselves settle this.   They queue up in a circle and each time the shadow of one of the parents falls in the entrance to the tunnel the queue moves round one, so each chick is fed in turn.

Distribution: Europe, Asia

GANG-GANG, THE GREY COCKATOO

THE grey cockatoo is known as the gang-gang because of its dreadful voice.

About a foot long, its body is greyish-brown but each feather is fringed with white. Its cheeks and head are a vivid scarlet and it has a crest of the same colour, which it raises in moments of excitement. The female is smaller and she has only a grey crest.

These cockatoos live in pairs or in flocks in the forest where their discordant cries can be heard throughout the day. They nest in holes in trees where the hen lays two or three white eggs, with no more nesting material than a few chips of wood. Both parents share in the rearing of the young, feeding them for about three months on half-digested fruit which they disgorge from their crops into the mouths of the nestlings.

The beak of a parrot or a cockatoo is enormously strong. The blue macaw, another member of the parrot family living in Brazil, is said to crush palm-nuts to a pulp with its beak while a man can only break them open with a heavy hammer. A pet parrot will soon bite to pieces any wooden object within reach, and this helps to explain how a pair of parrots or cockatoos make a hole in a tree for their nest—they hollow it out with their beaks.

Distribution: Eastern Australia

RED CARDINAL

A CARDINAL of the church wears a brilliant red robe, so it was natural to give this name to a bird that is a brilliant red all over, even on the beak. However, it is only the male that wears this resplendent dress, the hen being much duller, and, as is usual in the finch family to which cardinals belong, it is the hen that does most of the work in bringing up a family.

The nest is cup-shaped, made of twigs, leaves, grass and strips of bark, and is lodged in a vine, bush or low tree. The five or six eggs are white, marked with spots of brown or pale red, and they take a fortnight to hatch, the hen alone incubating them. When first hatched the chicks are nearly naked, with only a few wisps of down, and their eyes are closed. The hen feeds them by herself at first, but she is helped more and more by the cock as the next two weeks go by, at the end of which the young cardinals are able to fend for themselves.

The young are fed on insects which the parents first swallow and then, when the chick is ready for it, they bring the half-digested food up into the throat. The chick thrusts its beak into the parent's throat to take it.

Distribution: North America

BALD EAGLE

THE bald eagle is the national emblem of the United States of America. It stands three feet high and has a wing-span of six feet. It only looks bald, because although its body is brown its head is snow-white, as is its tail. The young eagles are all brown, and only gradually do the head and tail become white, and not until they are seven years old do they get all their white feathers.

The nest of sticks, grass and seaweed is on a cliff ledge or a hill-top near the sea, sometimes in a tree, and two white eggs are laid. Both parents take turns in sitting on the eggs, which hatch after five or six weeks. The downy eaglets are fed for ten weeks. The male eagle carries the food in his feet as he flies to the nest. The female then divides it up and gives pieces to each of the young eaglets in turn. The youngsters stay in or around the nest for another four to five weeks, by which time they have lost all their down and are clothed in their first brown feathers.

Distribution: Alaska, Canada, northern U.S.A.

BLUE JAY

ALL jays are noisy and the American blue jay is no exception to this. Most jays are brightly coloured, but there is none more colourful than the blue jay, patterned with black and white on the head, white patches and black bars on both wings and tail, and the whole set off by its white front.

Jays are bold and quick to defend themselves, using their sharp beaks or striking down with their strong clawed toes as they fly over their adversary, but they prefer to avoid a fight when possible and take refuge in the trees.

When they come to build their nest, these bold and courageous birds hide it. The blue jay builds a substantial nest of sticks, lined with fine grass and other soft materials, in a bush or low tree. Both cock and hen build, but only the hen incubates the four or five eggs which are mottled with grey and brown; but sometimes the cock feeds her during the two weeks or more that she is sitting on them. He is never far away at any time, and if danger threatens he launches a vigorous attack, and it has been known for the hen to leave the nest and join in. When the young are hatched both parents feed them for nearly three weeks.

Distribution: North America

LADY AMHERST
PHEASANT

THE native home of pheasants is Asia, and there are found many different kinds, all very beautiful. One of the most beautiful is the Lady Amherst pheasant. The cock is coloured delicately white, green and black, and his tail is nearly four feet long. He also has a dainty cape which he can raise to form a fan on either side to cover the neck and face. He does this when he is courting, and, as with all pheasants, he has several wives, which, although they are beautiful, are far less showy than the lordly cock pheasant.

It is a pity that the Lady Amherst pheasant has so little opportunity to show off its gorgeous feathers for it lives in inhospitable places and in the Himalayas sometimes as much as 15,000 feet above sea-level. The hen scrapes a hollow in the ground, lines it with a few bits of dry grass or leaves, and lays her eggs, which may number up to a dozen. She sits on the eggs for nearly a month, and when they hatch she alone looks after the chicks until, at about a fortnight old, they are able to take care of themselves.

Distribution: China

HOOPOE

THE hoopoe is dressed like a king but is brought up in a slum.

The feathers of the hoopoe are pinkish-brown, against which the wings and tail, which are black with white bars, show up boldly. The beak is long and slender, and curves slightly downwards, and on the hoopoe's head is a magnificent crest, like a Red Indian's head-dress. The feathers of this crest are tipped with black.

Hoopoes, which are nearly a foot long, lay their eggs in holes in trees or in crevices in buildings. As a rule they make no nest, although they may carry bits of straw, rags or feathers into the nesting chamber. The hen lays from five to eight whitish-grey eggs, and she alone sits on them for eighteen days, her mate bringing her food during this time. When the eggs first hatch the hen continues to brood the chicks, the cock still bringing food for her and the young ones. Later, both parents join in bringing insect grubs in their bills, and go on feeding the chicks in this way for three to four weeks.

Most birds keep their nests clean of droppings. Hoopoes do not; instead they carry in droppings, which is why we have said the nest is a slum.

Distribution: Europe, Asia, Africa.

PEREGRINE FALCON

IN a shallow scrape on a ledge or in a hole in a cliff, without nesting material, the peregrine falcon lays its three to four eggs, which are closely marked with reddish-brown blotches. The hen, known as the falcon, is nineteen inches long and is larger than her mate, the tiercel. The falcon takes the greater share of incubating the eggs but the tiercel does not neglect her. He feeds her while she is sitting, and does so by a kind of air-drop. Having caught a bird, the tiercel calls to the falcon, who leaves the nest and flies to meet him, either taking the prey from his feet in mid-air with her talons, or catching it as he lets it drop to her. At the end of a month the eggs hatch. The falcon continues on the nest, brooding the nestlings and being fed by the tiercel, but now she pulls some of the prey into small pieces to feed the young ones.

Distribution: World-wide

BARN OWL

A FEW years ago, a woman was pushing a perambulator down the street when a barn owl swooped at her. It was terrifying for the woman but the barn owl was only doing what she would have done if she thought that someone was going to harm her baby. She was getting in the first blow.

Barn owls are orange-buff on the back and white speckled with dark spots on the front. They sleep in barns and stables, in church towers or hollow trees, and that is where the hen lays her two white eggs. She makes little or no nesting arrangements for them, but if she takes no trouble over the nest she is none the less devoted to her owlets.

Not only do owls fiercely defend their youngsters, they also spend a good deal of their time on their upbringing. The eggs take just over a month to hatch and then follows a long period during which the owlets have to be fed. Young owls are particularly slow at learning how to hunt for themselves, and for eight or nine weeks the parents have to find food not only for themselves but for the two downy balls of fluffy white feathers with wide-open eyes that are always calling to be fed.

Distribution: Almost world-wide

Printed by Henry Stone & Son (Printers) Limited, Banbury
747.662